If You Didn't Want Grits,
How Come You Ordered Breakfast?

If You Didn't Want Grits, How Come You Ordered Breakfast?

Jake Vest

Sentinel Communications Company
Orlando/1990

To Bob, Sue, Judy and Rhonda who I grew up with; to R.V., who hasn't grown up yet and never will; to Dick and Mady, who let me marry their daughter; to my buddy Chuck, who, next to R.V., has inspired more cartoons than the house cat; to Randolph, who hired me for my first job and told me that one day I'd be a cartoonist; to Harry, who gives me Tennessee-Alabama football tickets; and to Dave, who passed up several excellent opportunities to fire me and who gave me my first golf clubs and a chance to do cartoons.

And to my wife, Laurie (Loretta to you folks who read cartoons), who puts up with much more than any woman ought to ever have to, and loves me in spite of it, for sharing me with a drawing board and a television set.

But most of all, to simply the two finest people I've ever had the privilege to know: my Momma and Daddy.

About the author, by the author

I was born in 1951 (footnoted in most history books as "the year nothing happened") in August, a slow month, known mainly around Tennessee as the last thing on the calendar between us and football season.

I'm the second son and third child of Jake and Edna Vest; they had a total of six between them and there was one stepchild. I wasn't the biggest — that'd be Robert, who we all called Bob. But I wasn't the littlest either. Rhonda got that. I wasn't the smartest — Sue had that honor nailed down no contest. I wasn't the prettiest (Judy), or the most ambitious (Ray, aforementioned stepbrother), or the most popular (Richard). I don't believe I was the ugliest or the dumbest either, but Richard, who now goes by RV, claims he isn't, and I know it's got to be one of us. In other words, I didn't stand out in a crowd, and believe me, our family was a crowd.

I grew up happy, which was an average thing to do back then, before kids had therapy and Nintendo. I was a decent second-baseman but not good enough to be shortstop; I could catch a football, but nobody would let me play quarterback; and I was just as good as anybody else around there at basketball.

I graduated from a medium-sized high school in Strawberry Plains at about the middle of my class. I started college in 1968 and was simultaneously a member of several anti- and pro-Vietnam War groups, depending on how pretty the recruiters were.

Then one day I got drafted — which was also a pretty average thing to have happen to you then. Since none of my kinfolk were senators from Northeastern states and we were too poor to have a doctor find something wrong with my spleen, I went into the Army.

I spent 143 years at Fort Polk, La., where I advanced to the rank of Pvt. E-2 along with several thousand other young baldheaded men. My tour of duty was in Korea, one of the very few places in the world of 1971 that didn't have a war going on.

For a little bit over a year I lived in a

half a chunk of pipe with people who would have trouble getting accepted into a good prison. I played a lot of poker, saw 600 movies, got drunk on 62 consecutive Friday and Saturday nights, received an Article 15 (sort of a junior court martial), got a broken nose in a fight, and did my Ugly American impersonation for any Korean national who could understand enough English to be insulted. In other words, I was a pretty average soldier.

After the army I finished college. Well, finished my GI Bill benefits anyhow. I never graduated but I took enough courses to, many of them journalism.

Which led to my first professional job as a copy editor in Columbus, Ga., which led me to my current job as a copy editor in Orlando, Fla. I write headlines and make sure the little tails on the commas are all pointed the same way. I've been doing this now for over a third of my life.

I used to hope I could sell out and get into public relations or something. What I really always wanted to be was the man at Campbell's who thinks up names for the soups — but as I get older, those kind of big dreams are starting to fade.

So that pretty much brings me up to where my life is right now. I'm pushing 40, I've got a 200 skajillion dollar mortgage on a house that grass won't grow around, and all my neighbors have dogs that holler all night.

I got a great wife, Laurie, who I call Loretta 'cause it irritates her and she's always good for cartoon ideas when she's irritated. She's near about as crazy as I am and tolerates many of my habits.

I'm a league bowler, I golf in the upper 90s to low to middle 100s, I hardly ever vote and I watch 14 hours of TV a day. My favorite food is the cheeseburger. I won't have a foreign car. I like to fish but I never get to do enough of it and I'm against flag-burning.

So I'd have to say I'm just about the most average person any of you are ever likely, or liable, to sit across a bar napkin from. Except for me doing this book, which I guess puts me in the company of Mark Twain and Balzac and Trixie Belden and those other literary giants. I hope I'm equal to it 'cause I think a lot of Trixie Belden.

Most of the things that happen to cartoon Jake either happened to me, or I was afraid they would happen to me, or I wish they'd happen to me, or they happened to somebody I know, or I heard about them happening to somebody I don't know. The other incidents are just stuff I made up.

'This is the most dangerous part of the evening
. . . I'm sober enough to remember her number,
and drunk enough to call.'

'Here we are . . . Anybody know how
to get down out of this thing?'

'If you didn't want grits, how come you ordered breakfast?'

'You boys better clean this puddle up . . . if it's
left overnight they'll build condos around it.'

'No doubt about it. You're gonna have to get
an American truck or a Japanese shotgun.'

'Well, it's after midnight and nobody'll dance
with us . . . we might as well start a fight.'

'I know I'm late, but I'm havin' car trouble
. . . I can't seem to recall
what I done with mine last night.'

'The snooze button is my favorite part of an alarm clock . . . I once slept 14 hours, five minutes at a time.'

Cowboy bad dreams.

'The last time somebody had that much trouble
getting up a hill it was Iwo Jima.'

'I'm not really huntin' . . . I just carry a gun
cause it makes my dogs feel important.'

'Looks like a beautiful warm sunny day . . . let's
go find a cold dark bar where we can enjoy it.'

'I been driving this thing for three years
and not a deputy yet has noticed
there's no license tag on it.'

'Must be a bad accident over there . . .
that looks like lawyers a-circling.'

'I hate to take the Christmas tree down . . .
it's the nicest piece of furniture I own.'

Warning to Northern relatives: It's a known fact that Florida residents can freeze to death at room temperature.

'I gotta get a new truck . . . the bus just won't stop for you when you're going huntin'.'

'Congratulations. It's hard to believe a man in your condition ever lived to be a man your age.'

'Stay away from that juke box . . . you ain't old enough to like anything that anybody in here will put up with.'

Portrait of a man who's fixin' to miss a golf ball.

How to kill a conversation in Aspen.

How women Christmas shop

How men Christmas shop

12

'Rodeo clown is just like any other job — it wouldn't be so bad except for the bull.'

Toughest Jobs in the World, No. 17 — Dental Hygienist for the National Wildlife Authority.

13

'I don't think you'll ever make any money on this scheme . . . country folks won't fall for it, and city folks won't understand the concept.'

'I got the only pit crew in NASCAR with self-service gas.'

'I'm too busy to have children — I got
a husband and a father to raise.'

'I was just demonstratin' to Leslie and Wayne
the wrong way to pick up a cat.'

'Probably gonna be the most important walk in
my whole life and I'm gonna have to make it
in rented shoes.'

'This marriage is off to a poor start — the groom
requested "Your Cheatin' Heart" and the bride asked for
"Don't Come Home a-Drinkin' With Lovin' on Your Mind." '

'We really appreciate you folks singin' along —
but we'd appreciate it even more if you'd sing
the same songs we're singing.'

'Don't get discouraged . . . remember, when
Cher first started going to the spa, she already
looked like Cher.'

'Don't look now, but your next opportunity
just met your last mistake.'

'It's just what I was lookin' for.
A jukebox that'll do 140.'

'Alcohol's never cured anything . . .
but then again, neither has aspirin.'

'There's two kinds of people in the world . . .
the kind that tip and the kind that
wish they could get another drink.'

'Them Johnson boys ain't real smart, but they sure do know how to train a huntin' dog.'

'Things would have been better for everybody if Sherman had left downtown Atlanta alone and just burnt the airport.'

'The coffee fund ain't seen a profit
since they put us on the honor system
and let us use our own cups.'

'You know it's gonna be a long morning when
you're just getting in from yesterday and
tomorrow's alarm clock is going off.'

'I spent a fortune on the driving range before I realized you didn't have to bring your own balls.'

'Between nutrition and etiquette, she's just about took all the flavor out of eating.'

'I like the sunshine just fine . . .
I just ain't too fond of being way up here
where it comes from.'

'When you consider what a wedding goes for
and how long a marriage lasts, I figure my last
son-in-law cost me about 30 bucks an hour.'

'An old-timer is anybody who can remember way back when the Interstate used to be finished.'

Warning: A woman can find out more embarrassing things about you in the first 10 minutes of a class reunion than she did in the last 10 years of being your constant companion.

'I hate checkups — if you give a good enough doctor
enough time and enough fancy equipment, he'll
eventually find something wrong with you that'll kill you.'

'The lawn won't grow for shucks,
but I do believe this is about as fertile
a driveway as I've ever seen.'

Conversations people have
when they get close to turning 40.

How monopolies work.

'I've spent more time in the water playing golf
than Lloyd Bridges did filming "Sea Hunt." '

'This is a sad night in the annals
of league bowling . . . we done been beat
by a team that didn't show up.'

'Sometimes you can tell on a first date
that a relationship ain't gonna work out.'

'Just for future reference, did you
happen to notice what the clearance was
on that underpass?'

'The lawyers get $150 an hour to argue, the judge gets $100,000 a year to listen, and us jurors get 10 bucks a day to make all the decisions — if there's justice goin' on here, it's plumb evaded me.'

'We find the defendant not guilty, but if it's at all possible we'd like to send his lawyer to jail.'

'This little tune's called "I'm Upwardly Mobile and Feelin' Kind of Low." '

'That's the trouble with omelets . . . two or three days later you have to throw the dishes away.'

'Our scorecard's not gospel accurate but
it's a pretty fair record
of what could have happened.'

'I was laid off three times last year, and still
worked more days than the post office.'

'Texas Tech versus Ole Miss in Shreveport . . .
wouldn't you love to have had the Red Man
concession for that game?'

'I don't need presents to have a happy holiday
. . . just let me stand in Momma's kitchen and
take a few deep breaths.'

'I wish 'em luck, but the way I look at it,
a marriage is just an engagement
that wasn't managed properly.'

'Architects must sit up all night trying to think up
stuff that builders can't do.'

'That's the trouble with wedding gifts —
we got 9,000 dollars worth of fancy dishes
and no table to eat off of.'

'It's easier to milk a cow
than it is to open these little cartons.'

'There's no way you can watch him swim and
still think mankind evolved from fishes.'

'Nothing can ruin a nice day
like spendin' eight hours of it
doin' what somebody else wants you to.'

Q: WHAT DO YOU CALL A 6 A.M. FOURSOME WITH JAKE IN IT?

A: A THREESOME

'Parked the truck in the pool, look like you shaved
with a chainsaw, got Loretta's shoes on —
something tells me you ain't a morning person.'

'What do you mean not rare enough? A good vet could still save this animal.'

'Sushi, huh? That's a relief. For a second, I thought that boy had served us raw fish.'

'It just don't pay to play Scrabble
with your Momma.'

'I'm sorry, you've got less than eight items —
you'll have to go wait in the fast lane.'

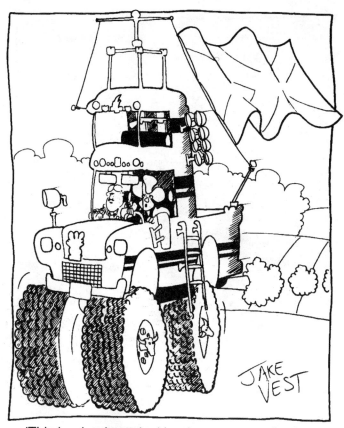

'This is what I was looking for . . . some simple, no frills, reliable transportation.'

How new home warranties work.

'A handy tip for moving — never let
your help get into the cold beer
until all the heavy stuff is upstairs.'

'We don't really want to exterminate the rats . . .
just coax them out of hiding and give them a good
talking to.'

'We can't hire nobody today . . . the lady that
gives our drug test is out drunk.'

What would happen if they let regular old
people like me and you on "Jeopardy"

Early signs that the economy
might be going bad.

What really happened at Appomattox.

'You just can't fry these boiler-bag meals.'

Two men in the early stages of deciding
that what they really wanted to do
was go out to dinner.

43

'Lemme go. When he realizes he hit me that hard
and didn't kill me, I think it'll break his spirit.'

'Must be a French restaurant . . .
Even the biscuits look like snails.'

'Forget it . . . Indiana Jones wouldn't
go in there after a golf ball.'

'He's a country singer who
dresses like a woman . . .
They call him Good Ol' Boy George.'

45

'Nothin' flushes one of these little rascals
like a truck horn.'

'I thought these little fellers
could use a good role model.'

'Here's what happens when you don't tell the contractors EXACTLY where to put the outlets.'

'Mind if we play through? We got a man back here getting married in an hour and we still gotta stop at a K mart somewhere and buy a ring.'

STEP 1: TAKE ALL THOSE SENTIMENTAL GEMS THAT CAN'T BE THROWN AWAY AND PACK THEM CAREFULLY IN UNMARKED BOXES...

STEP 2: THROW THE BOXES AWAY (YOU'LL NEVER MISS 'EM!)

Two Steps to More Efficient Moving.

Toughest Jobs in the World, No. 1369: Teaching somebody to drive a straight shift in Knoxville, Tenn.

'Floridians don't need winter weather to make them miserable . . . they got tourists for that.'

'Do we have to take 'em to Disney World? Couldn't we just put 'em through college or something?'

'How come everybody else's yard looks like the 18th green at Augusta and mine looks like the final turn at Churchill Downs?'

'I'd join you for more skiing except there's only two hours of daylight left . . . it'd take me that long to get all these clothes back on.'

'If they're "empty calories," how come they filled me out so good?'

'They not only won't pay for the food, they refuse to leave until you apologize for cookin' it.'

'Is this your pool, or is somebody cooking
a big pot of coconut fat people?'

'There ain't a house nowhere nice enough
to justify the trouble it takes
to move out of the one you're already in.'

'Not much pressure around here. In these parts, folks consider you a success if you die in a bigger trailer than the one you was born in.'

'At least he's quit throwin' his clubs when he misses a shot.'

'You really don't have to look over my shoulder, Sonny . . . I done retired from two jobs you won't ever be smart enough to apply for.'

'This ain't much more strenuous than running up and down a flight of stairs with a small cow under each arm.'

'Talk about good eatin' — if you was to put a
bowl of this chili on your head, your tongue
would beat your brains out trying to get at it.'

'How do you want your steak?
Rare, medium, or ruint?'

'That's not for me . . . if cowboys
was meant to fly, they'd put wings
on horses and bar stools.'

'I was drafted into the Army but I don't recall
being a murdering drug addict . . . I must have
been on K.P. the day we done all that.'

Why picking the right goal to defend
is essential in hillbilly basketball.

'I've spent several Januarys huntin' in Alaska, a few winters
skiing in Colorado and two Christmases soldiering in Korea
— but I never knew what cold was until I forgot her birthday.'

'Must be what they mean by the New South . . .
I just saw a BMW with a shotgun rack.'

Dentistry West of the Pecos.

'I'm gonna head out, Sam. If it was any duller in here, they'd put it on public television.'

'No matter how good the fiddles sound, you don't yell YEE-HAW at the symphony.'

'You must be here for the golf tournament . . .
just follow all the other fat men in funny britches.'

'The trouble with New Year's resolutions is you
make 'em one day too late to do you any good.'

How men plan weddings

How women plan weddings

'It's a typical ski outfit —
twice as much sweater as you can handle
and half as much britches as you need.'

Always remember, New York isn't any happier
about you being there than you are.

'Honey-lemon and strawberry creme rinse . . .
am I supposed to put this stuff on my head or
on my pancakes?'

'I hate it when a Roach Motel don't hold and
you gotta go in the kitchen at night and finish
one of these things off.'

'When I was a kid we were too poor
to buy M&Ms . . . we just had M's.'

'Destroyin' the universe again, are they?
Whatever happened to BB guns?'

'This is some pretty strong coffee, Bo . . . I've put three spoons full of creamer in it and it ain't changed color yet.'

'We're having a redneck triathlon — bowling, billiards and blackjack.'

'Somebody must have a hot date. I could smell
the Old Spice all the way out in the parking lot.'

'Let me guess who brought the individually
wrapped slices and the half-gallon
of Thunderbird.'

'The folks behind us are gettin' riled . . .
maybe we oughta start hittin' just one ball each.'

'I never buy a car made in a country
that's lost a World War.'

'If we'd been playing with eggs instead of golf balls, none of us woulda hit one solid enough to break it.'

'It's a small company . . . the two of us take turns being employee of the month.'

'Reporters don't write their own headlines. You got to understand the story to do that.'

Cow stress

'The plastic grocery bag is proof positive
that you don't have to think to have an idea.'

'I'm gonna spend the next week eating Spam and trail
mix and sleeping rolled up in a bag in the dirt . . .
good thing this is a vacation, if it was a job, I'd quit it.'

'This must be one of those tourist traps
that I heard about.'

'That's a lot of firepower, Bubba
. . . you planning on goin' hunting
or getting into politics?'

'I guess I can't complain . . . this old sweater held its shape longer than I did.'

'Eight hundred jillion people on Manhattan Island and not one single golf course . . . it's no wonder everybody's movin' to Florida!'

'If you want really expert tax advice, get it from somebody who's never paid any.'

'I don't need this . . . life's tough enough without somebody coming along and trying to simplify your job!'

How American business
puts technology to work

'I'd rather be smeared with Alpo and tossed into
a cage full of hungry pit bulls than spend a half
hour in the same house with a Chihuahua.'

'I always wondered how Loretta kept track
of all those special dates.'

'It's good to get back to Tennessee ever now
and again where people talk normal.'

'I get more exercise out of basketball than most people — after games, Loretta makes me come out here and bury my socks.'

'If he makes two or three putts in a row, everybody you know will have one of these things by this time next week.'

What Abner Doubleday probably had in mind

What Abner Doubleday probably
didn't have in mind

'I was not CREATIN' a disturbance . . . I was merely improving a disturbance that was already in progress.'

'Must be the aviator's special . . . only thing in here's a wing and a prayer.'

'Cheese is about the only food
I've ever run across that frying won't improve.'

'What do you mean stale? If this chicken salad
was any fresher it'd be egg salad.'

'The only way to improve on
homegrown tomatoes would be if they
grew at eye level, in the shade.'

'If they only sold swimmin' suits to people who
look good in 'em, there'd sure be a lot of nekkid
people on the beach.'

'Rigged it up myself . . . I just
can't abide tailgaters.'

'We got different memories of "The Good Old
Sixties" . . . you was trying to get into Sigma Chi,
I was trying to stay out of Mekong Delta.'

'A man ought to know his way around the
kitchen . . . when those eggs freeze,
it means the beer is cold enough to serve.'

'If you wash everything together in hot enough
water, you don't ever have to worry
about the colors matching.'

82

'Don't mess with him. His boy just quit the
football team and went out for soccer.'

'Garbagemen won't pick it up unless it's
wrapped, and I didn't have nothin' left
but these sandwich bags.'

'My Daddy was a mechanic, his brothers were
mechanics and my brothers are mechanics . . .
I guess you could say I was "Born to Lube."'

'I guess this is what they mean when they say
it's a buyer's market for condos.'

'These theme restaurants are okay,
but I like my excitement and my supper
served at separate tables.'

For the eighth year in a row, the Delaney Park
Over-40 Slam-Dunk Competition ends in
a 15-way tie for last place.

'Everybody around here used to be in the citrus business until the big freeze a few years back — now most of us are in the firewood business.'

The line drive is softball's way of reminding the third baseman to pay attention.

'You gotta be careful what you put on the
jukebox . . . old Lynyrd Skynyrd fans
are bad to have flashbacks.'

'We're gonna slow it down for the next few songs
while the paramedics haul off the cloggers who
tried to keep up with the last few songs.'

'Now I know why this place only got one star in the bed & breakfast guide.'

'I don't think the surgeon general knows about watermelon . . . it's about the only good thing left that hasn't been accused of killing people.'

'If you can't make money off tourists, Bubba,
you just ain't trying.'

Birthdays from hell

How the home-field advantage works
in cow-pasture football

'We had it custom designed to fit
my property . . . it's Olympic length,
but it's only Little League width.'

'Orlando to Atlanta, via Dallas and Tulsa with a layover in Nashville — there's no limit to what a man will put up with out of a pretty travel agent.'

By federal law, this plane will not be allowed to take off until ALL overhead bins are crammed full of junk and at least one baby starts squawling.

'You know, I really ought to take these mirrors off
when I'm not hauling a wide load.'

'I don't think Congress oughta get any kind of a
pay raise — in fact, if it was up to me,
I'd put 'em on commission.'

'Ever notice how the plushest hotels
always have the most pitiful plumbing?'

'It's just a settlement crack . . . nothing to worry
about . . . happens in all new houses.'

'Pretty aggressive . . . strong bite . . . won't let go
. . . heck, these things must be Pit Bullfrogs.'

Defensive driving in California

'A thunderstorm is Mother Nature's way of saying
you should have stayed at the Holiday Inn.'

Ways to Improve the Quality of Your Life, Part 1:
Don't go on long trips with anybody who's
learning to play the harmonica.

'Mobile Bay sure is a pretty piece of water,
but I have seen better surfing.'

'I had to give up basketball . . . I couldn't
handle the rejection.'

'We got the Wheel of Fortune home version
and it's my turn to be Vanna White.'

'Dang, this one's deserted too . . . I can't ever
seem to find a car wash open when I'm coming
home from the woods.'

'Us hardy Florida golfers know how to handle ourselves when the temperatures plunge way down into the low sixties.'

'It's a real low-budget airline. They stop here ever' now and again to get directions and use the bathroom.'

'There ain't nothing in this world happier than
a police officer with more equipment than he
knows how to use.'

'"If you don't pay us by Monday we'll scratch up your
truck, shave your dog, and turn your outhouse over..."
Now there's a collection agency that understands people.'

'This carpet's a little beyond shampooing . . .
you might want to plow it under
and plant a few tomaters in here.'

In prehistoric days, roving bands of men with
clubs spent their days hunting . . . in modern
times, at least they've improved the clubs.

'So I says "Judge, it seems to me like it's my own business whether or not I wear seat belts and what are you gonna do if I don't?"'

'This is their first try at putting on a bowl game — if it's a big enough success, next year they're gonna invite TWO teams.'

'A bowl this size don't rate TV cameras and a Goodyear Blimp — we get the Ferguson brothers with their Kodak Instamatic.'

'You know you're not in a "major" bowl game when they don't charge admission.'

'We're having an old-fashioned family holiday dinner . . . just me and a couple of my ex-wives and two or three of their current husbands and Lord only knows how many kids.'

'I guess "better late than never" don't apply to Christmas trees.'

Spinal Laryngitis — a condition that occurs
when you ain't got enough backbone
to keep your mouth running.

Why many employees pass up the opportunity
to get into middle management

'I hate to see anybody miss huntin' season, so I thought I'd turn a few ringnecks loose in here and let you have at 'em.'

'The way people went all moon-eyed over "Cats" we figgered this thing couldn't miss.'

'Yuppie frogs.'

'Me and Thelma Lou decided against having kids
— I was scared they'd look like her, and she was
scared they'd act like me.'

'Florida would probably be the best place in the whole world to play golf in the winter, if the whole world wasn't here playing golf.'

Why the pilgrims were so thankful when the Indians brought them that turkey.

'Why's there an $80 charge for parts and labor?
Because $80 is what we charge for labor
in these parts.'

On TV tonight: Descendants of the Charles Ingalls
family homestead in modern-day Southern California
on 'Little House on the Fairway'

'They're generally pretty well-behaved, but when these dogs want to go huntin', we go huntin'.'

'This contact lens solution may cause some initial discomfort . . . then again, it might just blister your eyeballs out.'

In-flight opera: An idea whose time never came

'We came up to Tennessee to watch the leaves change colors — at this speed, we may be here to see the first snowfall.'

'I ain't too much at the two-step — I'm physically capable, but the math is too much for me.'

'He might be bluffing . . . work your way around the table and see if his tail's wagging.'

Barbed wire — why the 'out pattern' isn't popular in cow pasture football

Lies people will tell to sell you a dog

Why the summer golf resort industry never really took off in southwest Texas

Legal technicalities

'This could be a valuable biology lesson . . .
we're fixing to find out if gators can climb and if
cowboys can fly.'

'Just shoo her away . . . that's a bad habit
she picked up from watching the cats.'

'This is my Titleist . . . I believe your
Pinnacle is over there next to that body.'

'I don't want to argue about the relative
merits of animals, but I can sell lizards
and folks can't give cats away.'

'I don't like being a bad golfer any better than
these people like waiting on me . . . but we're all
just gonna have to learn to live with it.'

'No law against being stupid —
if there was, I'd say we'd have
some fleeing felons on our hands.'

'Something tells me I ain't gonna
lead this league in rebounding.'

'We used to do this all the time back before
HBO cornered the market on bad movies.'

'THIS is too fancy? You don't want a tent,
you want an umbrella with doors on it.'

Deputy J. Edgar Bucknuckles interprets
the Constitution late one Saturday night
out on Route 46.

'You people want to quit rattling them breakfast dishes? . . . We got a man out here puttin' for birdie.'

'I'm making a fashion statement but people are laughing too loud to hear it.'

119

'He's been sitting out there with a baloney sandwich for two days just waiting on our first tomato to get ripe.'

Trouble on a cattle drive just outside Paris, Texas

The last thing Winford Hawkins ever saw in
this life after he scurried onto the driving range
to retrieve his errant tee shot

'I don't generally care for theater, but the boys
here were really looking forward to this one.'

Seth Hawkins and Old Blue — the entire tourism
industry of East Bear Track, North Carolina.

'I think I got a good shot, but I can't recall
which table I was playing on.'

'There's three beers left in the cooler
and I haven't used my mulligan yet
. . . WE AIN'T LEAVING!'

'It's a TV show about two good-ol'-boy brothers
who bootleg atomic warheads . . . they call it
The Nukes of Hazzard.'

123

'Nothin's wrong with the machinery
. . . after that last frame, your ball's
just ashamed to come back.'

'Moving 800 miles to a new state on short notice
wasn't any trouble at all next to getting the
address changed on a driver's license.'

'Society officially went to heck the first time
a farmer went hungry and a lawyer didn't.'

'If Payne Stewart was to ever see you
in that get-up, he'd start playin' golf
in overalls and a trenchcoat.'

Most Useless Things in the World, No. 6:
A morning traffic report during rush hour

'Mia Farrow and Alan Alda in a Woody Allen
movie — this might be the biggest waste of $20
since you sent your cat to obedience school.'

'Our 24-hour service don't start till 7 a.m.'

'That's pretty typical —
looks like a million, averages 105.'

'I reckon we ain't successful yet either
— we still worry more about groceries
than we do about taxes.'

The First Rule of Rural Motoring:
Never drive down a dirt road
you ain't willing to walk back up.

'If you didn't spend at least 8 hours diggin' a hole or swingin' a hammer, there ain't nobody in here interested in how bad a day you had.'

'Fifteen minutes ain't much when you're late, but it sure is a long time when you're waiting.'

No trip to the San Francisco area is complete without a stop off in wine country.

'It's only happy hour . . . can you imagine
what he's like by last call?'

'I've bought three sets of golf clubs since the last
time I bought a mower . . . but, then again, I ain't
tryin' to improve the quality of my mowing.'

'About 40 gallons of varnish and 800 sheets of sandpaper ago, buying unfinished furniture seemed like a good idea.'

'There's a jillion formats, but there's only two kinds of radio station — the kind that plays Merle Haggard regularly and the kind I don't listen to.'

Why our soon-to-be 50-year-old nuclear
deterrent force don't seem to scare people
as much as it used to

'That's got all three qualifications for a good golf
shot — we can find it, it's dry, and it's closer to
the hole than it was before he swung at it.'

'There's a million options, but people our age
have only got two real choices: You can be fat,
or you can be hungry.'

'If I thought for a second you were the best I was
gonna do for company this evening, I'd go home
and clip my toenails and watch "Mr. Ed" reruns.'

'That's the most people I've ever seen asleep
in a movie that wasn't directed by Woody Allen.'

Low Points in High Art: The Pike County players
try to broaden their fund-raising base by staging
a live production of 'Smokey and the Bandit.'

'You might do a better job of cutting if you emptied that bag a little more often.'

'Lorena was my first wife and Flora was Number 3 and Kitty was in between — I guess that makes her a midwife, and those 6 months we were together was my "midwife crisis." '

'If you pay more'n two dollars for a bottle of wine you're just wasting your money on a fancy label.'

'I'd heard cockroaches were supposed to take over the world but I didn't realize they were gonna start with your apartment.'

Grocery shopping in Lafitte, Louisiana

Reasons to quit drinking, No. 73: Because after nine beers, this looks like a fair fight.

'You ought to go home and rest up.
What are you saving your sick leave for
anyhow? Your funeral?'

'Save those tin foil scraps, they might come in
handy — you can never tell when we might want
to add a room onto the Winnebago.'

'Why yes . . . as a matter of fact, we are driving
a convertible . . . how did you know?'

'I know how to use every tool I own,
and I own every tool I know how to use.'

'You know it's not been a real good checkup when the doctor who done it offers you a cigarette.'

'This is my new exercise routine . . . first I do a few laps, then I lap a few down.'

'I guess the lesson here is: "Never try to haul a great big chunk of plywood on a little bitty truck when the wind's blowing."'

'Let me get this straight . . . you ride around on that two-wheel death trap and give tickets to people who don't have their seat belts buckled?'

'It's 4 a.m., we're way beyond thinking and
almost can't talk — let's call somebody.'

'Ever' time I think I've got my finances in order, some
unexpected expense comes up . . .
like rent, or a weekend.'

'Oh good, coupons. I was afraid for a minute
I'd get out of here in time for supper.'

'I guess you could call this half a mistake —
we all intended to get drunk,
but none of us meant to be hung over.'

'I'd rather fight Mike Tyson AND Buster Douglas in
a crowded elevator than spend a day trying to
amuse an 8-year-old with an imagination.'

'I'm gonna go sleep in the bathtub — I don't
think I'll ever be able to relax under
a ceiling fan that I personally installed.'

'We're doing "Orange Blossom Special"
— as usual, his train's running
about 5 minutes late.'

'It's a real small business,
but they throw away better tomatoes
than any city store can get hold of.'

Why a hook is more dangerous in
horseshoes than it is in golf

'Done properly, the Texas Two-Step is just like
Roller Derby except with no wheels.'

A husband who's fixing to get in trouble
and won't ever understand the reason why

The only problem with full-size American trucks

'Sorry, a new truck is not like a new puppy — it can't spend the first few nights inside.'

'Pretty good shootin' there, Daniel Boone . . . maybe you ought to call in an air strike.'

'I hate it when the bowling alley closes
before they get all their bets settled.'

A wine-tasting in Apopka, Fla.

'I don't know which is more dangerous
in a hairstylist — an imagination
or a sense of humor.'

Stupid questions

The End